Lorna Bailey – The First Mi

"This is a book of my early designs. If you are already a collector of my work, then I hope you enjoy revisiting these designs, perhaps seeing variations that you may not have seen before. If you are new to my work, then I hope you will find this book to be a good introduction to designs that are close to my heart. They have allowed me to develop my ideas further than I could ever have imagined. I look forward to the opportunity of meeting you if you ever make it to any of our future Collector's Club events. In the meantime, let me take you on a tour of my designs. Enjoy!"

Lorna Bailey

Edited by Dave Lee

FIRST PUBLISHED IN GREAT BRITAIN IN 2001 BY

LJB CERAMICS
OLD ELLGREAVE POTTERY
NEWCASTLE STREET
BURSLEM
STOKE-ON-TRENT
STAFFORDSHIRE
ST6 3QF
ENGLAND
UK

A catalogue record for this book is available from the British Library

ISBN 0-9541214-0-6

Printed in Great Britain by Pelican Press

Foreword by Eric Knowles

I have to admit that I was a latecomer to the talents of Lorna Bailey, and by the time we eventually met face to face she had recently attained the grand old age of *twenty*. Working as I do on the fringes of that strange world called show-business I have become a seasoned sceptic of hype and adulation, and consequently I decided to adopt a cautious approach. What should I expect? Would she prove to be precious, egotistical or a precocious wild child? Rumour had reached me that she was being tipped for Stoke-on-Trent's Sentinel newspaper Business Woman of the Year award. Would I be meeting a power-suited, expensively coiffured woman to whom time was money; and after giving me the benefit of so many minutes of her time, would send me off whilst wishing me "a nice day"?

When the moment of truth arrived I was met by a casually dressed woman whose youthful appearance would have most public house bar staff demanding proof of I.D. before serving her a gin and tonic. In a short period of time I came to the conclusion that I was in conversation with a totally unpretentious young woman who obviously benefited from the virtue of simply being "normal".

It wasn't until my visit to the pottery that I was able to fully appreciate the extensive range of output emanating from the fertile imagination of just one person. Prior to my trip to the Potteries I was determined to keep an open mind as to the virtues, or otherwise, of this new pottery whiz kid who commanded admiration from a collector's club of two thousand that was helping to keep the order books nice and full.

Like it or not the comparison with Clarice Cliff was hard to ignore, but I was mindful of the fact that Miss Cliff had herself been open to outside influences. In fact, any student of her output knows only too well of the inspiration provided by Edouard Benedictus, Josef Hoffman and Amedeo Modigliani. A more careful analysis of Lorna's work revealed a style that was far more distinctive and individualistic than I had initially credited her with. Her pots were obviously the efforts of a free spirit that, like most young women of her age, simply wanted to have fun. The use of bold underglaze colours applied to inventive designs and translated on to humorous or outrageous shapes all add to the finished product deserving of the accolade "a good humoured pot by Lorna Bailey".

Long may she have fun!

Contents

Wafer vase (Stoke-on-Trent), Back-to-Back salt and pepper (Pagoda Garden), Upside Down 2 Semi-Circle Vase (Inglewood).

Previous page: The Eric Knowles vase. 50 were produced, some specially signed by Eric.
The first one was sold at a special auction for £190/$280.

Introduction

I think that Lionel thought it would only take a few weeks to produce this book, and, as I write this, is probably wondering why it isn't finished yet. Hell, I'm working on it right now! If only I knew then what I know now. I remember that first meeting with Lorna and her dad Lionel, and my naivety, not realising that it was going to be *me* sifting through all those archives and photos.

This book is not the definitive book on every piece Lorna Bailey and LJB Ceramics have produced. I wonder if that book will ever exist. The combinations of some designs are so complex, they are sometimes hard to even describe in words, let alone compile photographically. The set of shapes, the changes in design, the colourways, the prototypes, the sleepers, the specials, the one-offs... my cause is lost!

No, this book is just a flavour of Lorna's work - I could have said Lorna's *early* work, but it feels so recent (and Lionel, being Lionel, tells me that a few of these pieces are still available). And yes, the book's title is very tongue-in-cheek, but I wasn't prepared to call a 23 year old's first book "Lorna Bailey – The Early Years". Although, come to think of it...No, we're not changing the name now!

The prices, sizes and rarity information should just be taken as a guide; and if we've missed anything out, well, it'll just be an excuse to do another book. Now, is that a problem? Current values are based on recent auction prices, but what is rare is not always expensive. Where no current value is given, add 20% to the original price.

Thanks must go to everyone at LJB Ceramics, especially Lorna, Lionel, Jennifer, Claire, and Warren for helping me compile their book for them. Guys, I'm tired and I want to go to bed now. Also thanks to John Lawton, Vic Jelenski, Mike & Janet of Yesterdays and Lee Sherratt for use of their photographs.

And all my love to Michelle for her constant encouragement! (Only she can tell you how many times I said, "I give up!")

Dave Lee is a Publications Consultant and the author of The Wade Dynasty. He lives on the edge of Stoke-on-Trent.

A special smiling clock teapot colourway - Auction price £600/$900 (1999, BarryCotton auction)

A brief history of Lorna Bailey and L.J.B. Ceramics

In 1995 she was earning pocket money in her spare time, painting in her dad's new pottery works. Yet in January 1999, a few days short of her 21st birthday, Lorna Bailey received a letter telling her that she had been short-listed for the Midlands Business Woman of the Year award. Even Lorna finds this meteoric rise from student to acclaimed designer hard to believe sometimes. But her talent and her vision were recognised early on by collectors and associated businesses, as you will be able to see from the founding designs in this book.

The source for her inspiration was all around her as she was growing up. Born on 10th February 1978, she has lived her whole life in and around the Wolstanton area of Newcastle-under-Lyme, and it is this area from which the majority of the names for her designs are taken. From *Oaklands*, where she went to nursery school, to Wolstanton High School, which is between *Dimsdale Hall* and *May Bank*. And between Oaklands and Dimsdale are the prestigious *Watlands* and *Park Avenue*... the list goes on and on.

From school she attended Stoke-on-Trent College, the successor to the Burslem School Of Art where Lorna`s illustrious predecessors in design had all studied; namely Clarice Cliff, Susie Cooper, Mabel Leigh, Fredrick & Charlotte Rhead and many more. Because of Lorna's often bold and striking designs she is often compared to her forebears. But those who might claim she replicates their work clearly haven't studied her designs, which as you can see for yourself have their own wonderful and distinct style.

After gaining a B.Tec National Diploma in Design (Ceramics), she linked up with her father's new business, L.J.B. Ceramics, which came about whilst Lorna was still a student at College. A major local pottery, Woods Potters of Burslem, had gone into liquidation, and its assets were being sold off. At the same time the owner of Artone Pottery which rented part of the Old Ellgreave Pottery (coincidentally where Charlotte Rhead had worked whilst at Wood & Son) was seeking to retire. Accordingly her father, Lionel, with friend Geoff Stanway, purchased a large amount of Woods Assets, took over the Old Ellgreave Pottery and set up business, initially producing traditional hand painted wares, e.g. Toby Jugs & decorated ware. Lorna spent all her spare time, when not at college, working in the business earning her pocket money by painting for the business and experimenting with her own designs.

Over a period of time trade buyers, who frequently visited the premises, gradually started taking an interest in Lorna's work, in addition to the more traditional wares. They shrewdly reckoned there was a market for these colourful pieces. Slowly sales of Lorna's work increased so that by early 1998 Lorna and two of the hand painting staff were producing work exclusively designed by Lorna. However, things took off in a big way when journalist Lorne Spicer of "Collect It!" Magazine met Lorna at the 1998 Ceramic Showcase, where she was exhibiting her latest designs. Lorna's work had been turning up at Collector's Fairs all over the country, and Lorne was anxious to meet this new young designer. From this first meeting came a commission for the magazine, 250 Astro Rocket sugar sifters to be offered to readers of the July edition. The commission sold out within hours of the magazines hitting the streets, and accordingly a further commission of 250 Bud Vases was agreed for the next issue. This edition sold out before the magazine officially reached the newsagents! Suddenly Lorna and Lionel had a phenomenon on their hands.

LORNA DRAWING AT SCHOOL INSIDE HER HOME-MADE PICTURE FRAME

THE EVENING SENTINEL
NORTH STAFFORDSHIRE & SOUTH CHESHIRE
BUSINESS WOMEN OF THE YEAR 1998

Lorna with rare Park Avenue charger (see page 62)
Photograph courtesy of 'Collect it!' magazine.

The demand for information on Lorna became so great that a Collector's Club was formed which soon grew to over 2000 members world-wide. The family business expanded and moved into new premises nearer Burslem, Ellgreave House. Lorna's mother Jennifer ran the office, the Collector's Club and the new factory shop; whilst brother Warren was drafted in as Site Manager. The pace was hectic to say the least, but soon the Club was shipping Lorna's exclusive Limited editions around the world to thousands of eager collectors.

Just as preparations were being made to celebrate Lorna's 21st birthday, that letter arrived. Two months later at a special ceremony, Lorna was awarded The Evening Sentinel Business Woman of the Year for 1998. It was a stunning achievement for her and her family, and deserved recognition for her creativity and hard work.

Since then the business has grown and grown, but has never lost the human touch. The family hosts bi-annual open days at the factory for their club members who come from all over the world to be there. Lorna spends most of her time at the Ellgreave works, but frees herself up to work on new and exciting designs, each more stunning and extraordinary than the ones before. But what is more extraordinary is that she is still in her early 20s. What amazing designs are there still to come?

FOR MORE INFORMATION, CONTACT:

THE LORNA BAILEY COLLECTOR'S CLUB,
LJB CERAMICS,
OLD ELLGREAVE POTTERY,
NEWCASTLE STREET,
BURSLEM,
STOKE-ON-TRENT,
STAFFORDSHIRE, ST6 3QF,
ENGLAND, UK.
OR VISIT www.lorna-bailey.co.uk

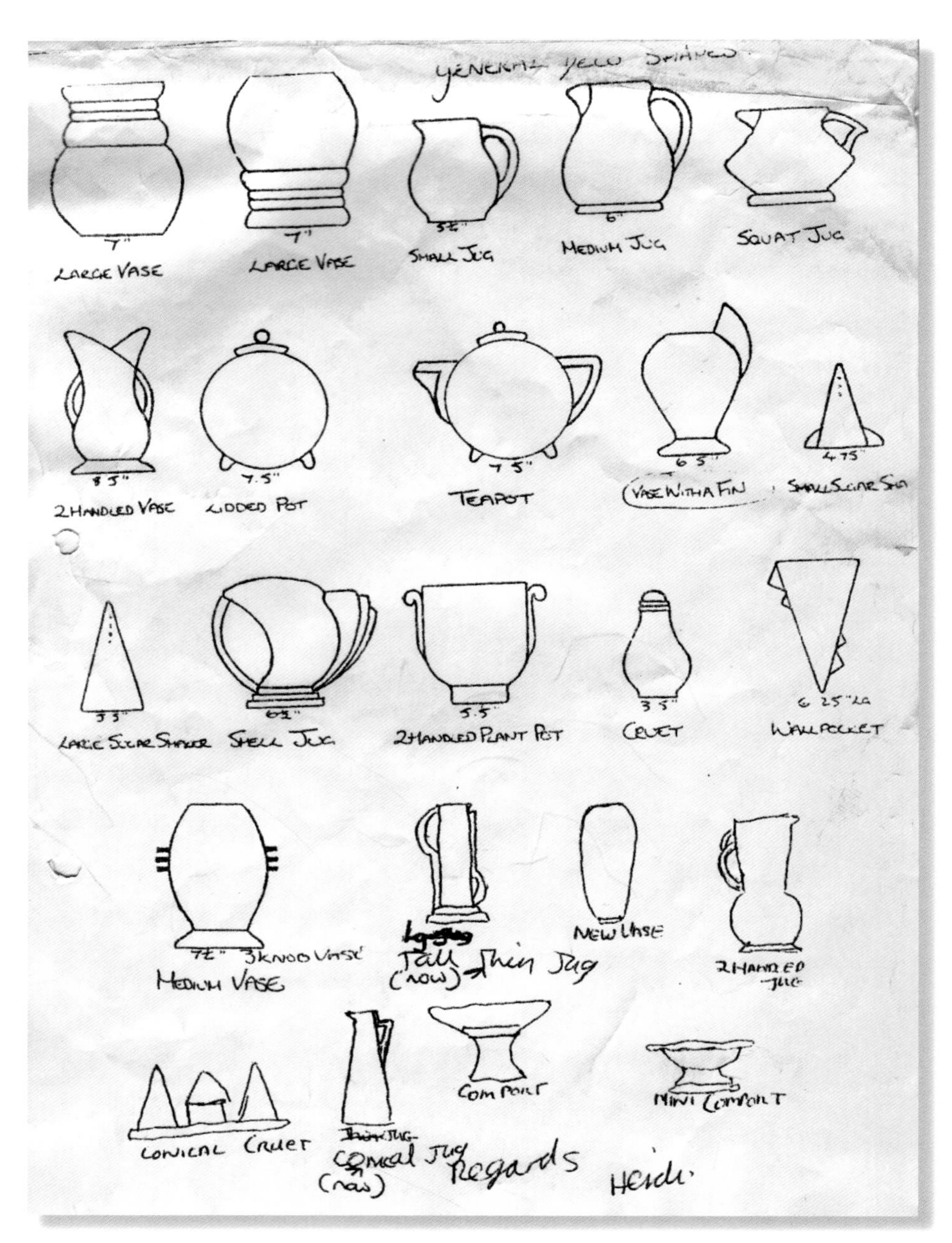

Lorna's drawings of early shapes, with Lionel's additional drawings at the bottom of the page

LIST OF SHAPES

This is a key to the shapes that were (and in some cases still are) available with Open Stock items:

Conical wallpocket Hexagon
Fin vase (discontinued 6/98)
Finned sugar shaker
2 Handled Planter (discontinued 8/98)
Tall Thin Vase (discontinued 8/98)
2 Handled Jug £40/£45 ($60)
2 Handled Vase £40/£45 ($60) (discontinued 6/99)
3 Knob Vase £36/£40 ($55) (discontinued 6/99)
Large Comport £40/£45 ($60)
Conical Cruet £36/£40 ($55) (discontinued 8/99)
Cruet £14/£16 ($21) (discontinued 8/99)
Large Conical Jug £40/£45 ($60) (discontinued 8/99)
Large Sugar Shaker £18/£20 ($27)
Large Vase £40/£45 ($60)
Large Vase (Upside down) £40/£45 ($60) (discontinued 8/99)
Lidded Pot £36/£40 ($55) (discontinued 12/99)
Medium Jug £30/£35 ($45) (discontinued 6/99)
Mini Comport £30/£35 ($45)
Round Teapot £40/£45 ($60)
Shell Jug £36/£40 ($55)
Small Jug £20/£25 ($30) (discontinued 6/99)
Squat Jug £36/£40 ($55) (discontinued 6/99)
Tall Thin (Deco) Jug £40/£45 ($60) (discontinued 8/99)
8 piece miniature tea (or coffee) set £50/£60 ($75)
Small Conical Jug £30/£35 ($45) (discontinued 8/99)
½ Wallpocket £36/40 ($55)
¾ Vase £50/60 ($75)
¾ Wallpocket £40/45 ($60)
Bowl £40/45 ($60)
Full Vase £60/70 ($90)
Full Wallpocket £50/55 ($75)
Large Wallpocket £60/65 ($90)
Wafer Vase £40 ($60) (8/99 – 12/99)
Deco Jug £45 ($70) (Introduced 6/99)
2 Semi-circle Vase £40 ($60) (6/99 – 12/99)
Back to Back Salt & Pepper £30 ($45) (Introduced 6/99)
Rocket Sugar Shaker £25 ($37)
Wafer Vase £40 ($60) (Introduced 6/99)
Rocket vase £48 ($72)
Back to Back 2 Handled Vase £45 ($70) (Introduced 6/99)
Back to Back 3 Knob Vase £45 ($70) (Introduced 6/99)
Back to Back Squat Vase £45 ($70) (Introduced 6/99)
Octagon Vase £40 ($60) (Introduced 8/99)
Fluted Vase (3") £35 ($55) (Introduced 8/99)
Fluted Vase (2") £30 ($45) (Introduced 8/99)
Oblong Vase (3") £35 ($55) (Introduced 8/99)
Small Oblong Vase (2") £30 ($45) (8/99 – 12/99)
Upside Down 2 Semi-Circle Vase £40 ($60) (Introduced 8/99)
Lipped Wafer Vase £40 ($60) (8/99 – 12/99)
½ pint Coffee Pot £25 ($37)
1 pint Coffee Pot £35 ($55)
1½ pint Coffee Pot £40 ($60)
2 pint Coffee Pot £45 ($70)
½ pint Tea pot £25 ($37)
¾ pint Tea Pot £30 ($45)
1 pint Tea Pot £35 ($55)
1 ½ pint Tea Pot £40 ($60)
2 pint Tea Pot £45 ($70)
Giant Sugar Shaker £40 ($60)
Large Conical Vase £45 ($70) (Lava only)
Egg cups £5 ($8)
Tall cruet (pair) £18 ($27)
Square Based Sugar Shaker £20 ($30)
Triangular Based Sugar Shaker £20 ($30)

Where two prices appear, the item was for sale pre-1998 for the former price. (Note that some of the early shapes and commissions were never sold directly to collectors, and so retail price varied.)

Fin vase (rare rainbow handle),
Conical Wallpocket and (front left)
Large Vase (Upside down) (House and Path),
Finned Sugar Shaker and Cruet (rare early design);
Squat Jug and Small Jug (Dingle)
(Note that the bush on the Small Jug is not on later Dingle pieces).

Open Stock

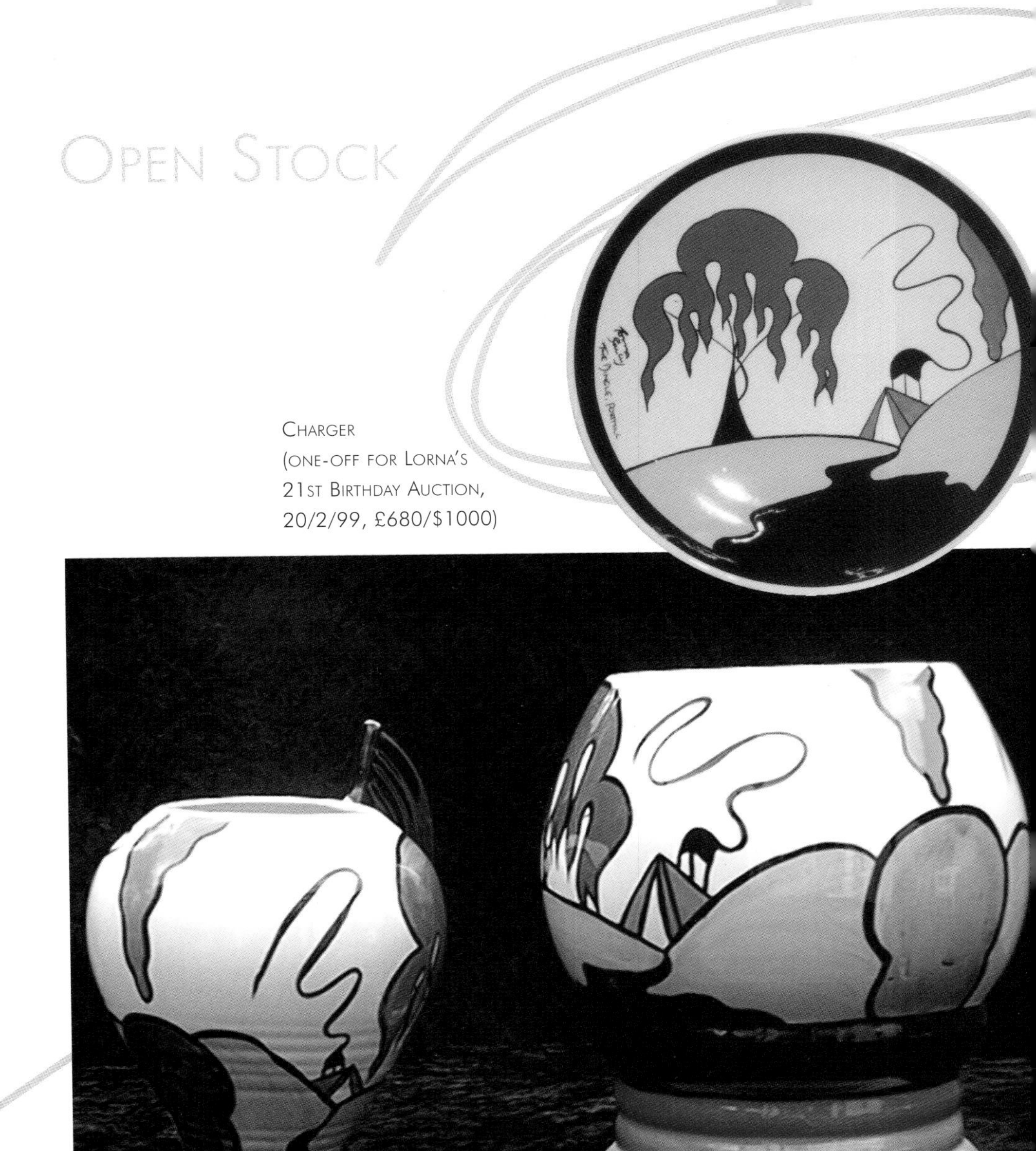

Charger
(one-off for Lorna's
21st Birthday Auction,
20/2/99, £680/$1000)

Fin vase and Large vase (upside down)

Open Stock

Bridge & Stream

Mar 96 – Feb 99

"As Bridge & Stream was in production for a number of years, the design changed. For example, it originally had four trees on the left of the bridge; which went, in order, red, yellow, orange and then red again. This then became three trees, and then finally two trees. The cut in trees was simply to keep up with public demand!" (Lorna)

Rare picture of sugar shaker with 3 trees.

Originally depicted on a limited number of early shapes, but later available in the standard set (see List of Shapes). Particularly rare: Differing Sugar Shakers, particularly finned versions.

2 Handled jug, finned sugar shaker, Large Vase

Lidded pot and Shell jug

Circus

Aug 96 – June 98

"Circus was based on the fringe of a circus tent. The original design had several coloured tines hanging down, not just the 3 or 4 that later pieces had. Some had coloured bands around the base of the shape. Unfortunately, it didn't sell too well, which makes most of the pieces particularly rare!" (Lorna)

A selection of 'Circus' pieces and yellow colourways.

Available in the standard set of shapes (see List of Shapes). Particularly rare: Circus is very sought-after, particularly early versions of the design with narrow tines. The miniature tea/coffee sets can fetch £300-£650/$500-$1000 (eBay auction).

CARNIVAL

Aug 96 – June 98

"Carnival originally sold even less than Circus, which makes the design especially collectable. The design gave the feeling of a carnival with streamers or a ticker-tape parade. Later pieces in certain shapes had black and orange bands around the top." (Lorna)

TWO HANDLED VASE (LEFT), WHILST THE COLOURWAY (RIGHT) WAS SOLD AT THE NEWARK FAIR (SEE COMMISSION PIECES)

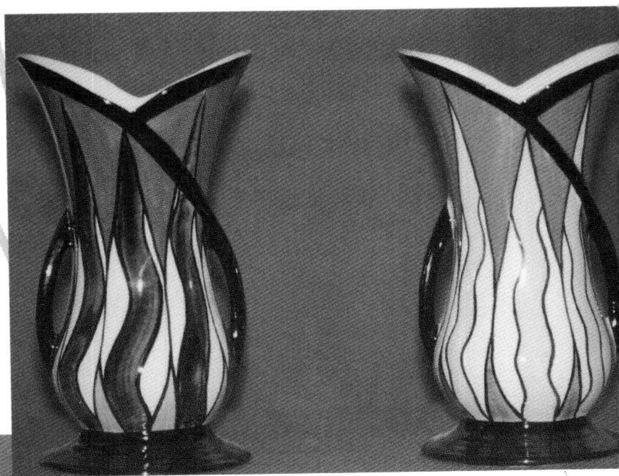

FIN VASE, SUGAR SHAKER AND CANDLESTICK (NOTE ORANGE AND BLACK BANDS)
(SEE ALSO THE PICTURE ON PAGE 22, WHICH SHOWS A SHELL JUG IN THE CARNIVAL DESIGN)

Available in the standard set of shapes (see List of Shapes). Particularly rare: Carnival is the most sought-after pattern, particularly the candlesticks and sugar shakers (£210/$300, Jan 2000, Ash auction).

Picture shows Bridge and Stream on the teapots (¾ pint, 1 pint, 1½ pint) on the right and the comport on the left. The teapots on the left depict the Beach design. The ½ pint teapot and ½ pint coffee pot in the middle depict the Circus design, and the shell jug on the right is Carnival (£140/$200, Sept 2000 auction). The Tall Thin Jug at the back is in the Stoke-on-Trent design.

TUBE-LINED SQUAT JUG

Mar 96 – Dec 98

"These were produced at the Old Ellgreave Factory, and sold very well " (Lorna)

2 WHITE SQUAT JUGS, A BLUE JUG AND A GREEN JUG

Available in the following shapes:

Blue/Green Dahlia Squat Jug £40/45 ($60/70)
Blue/Green Lily Squat Jug £40/45 ($60/70)
White Dahlia Squat Jug £36/40 ($55/60)
White Lily Squat Jug £36/40 ($55/60)

Particularly rare: One-offs such as the Squat jugs with a Burgundy coloured background

PAGODA

Aug 96

"Very limited production. Only about 20-25 pieces were ever made, and most are with my family in Aberdeen." (Lorna)

PROTOTYPE CHARGER (£1,100/$1,600, APRIL 2000 AUCTION)

Available in a VERY limited number of shapes (see List of Shapes). Particularly rare: Everything!!

CHARLES RENNIE MACKINTOSH

Dec 96 - 2001

"Charles Rennie Mackintosh was an innovative designer at the turn of the 20th century. This was an interpretation of his designs." (Lorna)

PICTURE SHOWS ALL 5 PIECES PRODUCED IN THIS DESIGN

Only available in the following shapes:

June 97 – Lge Vase, £50/55 ($75/85)
Sm Vase, £40/45 ($60/70)
Bud Vase £24/28 ($35/40)
Nov 97 – Lge Plant Pot £40/45 ($60/70)
Sm Plant Pot £ 30/35 ($45/50)

Particularly rare: The narrow-necked bud vase that was produced for only a few months. (see photo, right. The squat jug and tall vase are prototypes – no more than three or four were produced.)

Open Stock

Chetwynd

Dec 96 – June 98

"Produced in memory of Colley Shorter, husband of Clarice Cliff, whose homes were all called Chetwynd. I used actual Shorter moulds for the jug and the vase, but the design was my own colourway." (Lorna)

Large and Small Candlesticks, toast rack and a vase.
(Later toast racks had a house painted on.)

Only available in the following shapes:

Vase, £40/$60, Jug, £40/$60;
July 99 - Lge Candlesticks £30/35 ($45/50),
Sm Candlesticks £24/28 ($35/40), Toast Rack £20/25 ($30/35)

Particularly rare: The 8 sugar shakers that were produced for the Shepton Mallet fair (£150+/$250+). The vase fetches £120+/$200+ at auction.

DECODENCE RANGE:

FLAPPER, BAUHAUS, SHOWTIME

June 96 - 2000

"Decodence was my last major project for College in June 96. It has been in production since the business started." (Lorna)

4 WALLPOCKETS, AND A VASE (BAUHAUS IS TOP LEFT, SHOWTIME IS TOP CENTRE, THE REST ARE FLAPPER)

Only available in the following shapes:

½ Wallpocket £36/40 ($50/60),
¾ Vase £50/60 ($75/90), ¾ Wallpocket £40/45 ($60/70),
Bowl £40/45 ($60/70), Full Vase £60/70 ($90/100),
Full Wallpocket £50/55 ($75/80), Large Wallpocket £60/65 ($90/100)

Particularly rare: Colourways. For example, an early colourway of Bauhaus was in purple, green and black.

Stoke-on-Trent

Aug 97 –

"Based on Stoke's bottle ovens and the Cauldon Canal. Initially the design was available in almost every shape, until it was realised that the black bottle ovens didn't always look so good on things such as the Two Handled Vase, the Large Vase, and the Squat Jug; only one or two of these were ever made." (Lorna)

Tall thin deco jug, conical jug, small conical jug, sugar shaker; lidded pot, round teapot, shell jug
See also picture on page 22, which shows the Tall Thin Deco Jug

Available in the standard set of shapes (see List of Shapes). Particularly rare: Early shapes such as the Two handled vase, Large vase and Squat Jug. Most shapes are still in production.

Beach

Oct 97 – Mar 99

"This was probably a hint to my Dad that I needed a holiday! I wanted something with a positive summer feel, and this proved particularly popular." (Lorna)

2 handled planter and Tall Thin vase

See also the picture on page 22, which shows three different sized tea-pots

Available in the standard set of shapes (see List of Shapes). Particularly rare: Sugar shaker. Beach is becoming more and more sought-after (for example 2 handled planter worth approximately £120/$200).

Deco Lady Vase & Bowl

Oct 97 (small vase and bowl)
June 99 – June 2000 (Large vase)

"This was an existing mould from a bankruptcy sale on which I did a design colourway. It proved so popular that it was 'copied' - shall we say - by other companies." (Lorna)

Small vase and bowl

Small Vase is 4.5" high, and the dish is 7.5" diameter.
Small Vase and dish - £28/$40 each.

LARGE VASE

Stag range

Jan 98

"This was another mould from a bankruptcy sale. The design was sort of 1950s retro, and it was only available in three vases and a dish." (Lorna)

Stag vase (original price £40/$60)

STAG COLOUR PROTOTYPE

Particularly rare: All of them! (£100+/$150+)

Pharaoh Comport

Jan 98

"Extremely rare, even some of the top collectors don't have the Pharaoh Comport. The original price was about £50/$75, but it is now worth about £400/$600." (Lionel)

Marshland Cottage

July 98-June 99

"This design replaced The Dingle, Porthill. Marshland Cottage is based on Wolstanton Marsh. The bush disappeared off later versions. Early sugar shakers had the complete design on, but later ones only had a subset of the design." (Lorna)

Large vase (Upside down), Two handled jug, Tall thin jug, Two handled vase; 3 Knob vase, sugar shaker, shell jug
See also picture on page 37, which shows mini coffee set

Available in the standard set of shapes (see List of Shapes). Particularly rare: Discontinued shapes such as old wall pocket and finned sugar shaker.

Open Stock

Inglewood

Mar 99 - Aug 99

"Inglewood is a small road in Porthill opposite The Dingle. The design replaced the House & Path design." (Lorna)

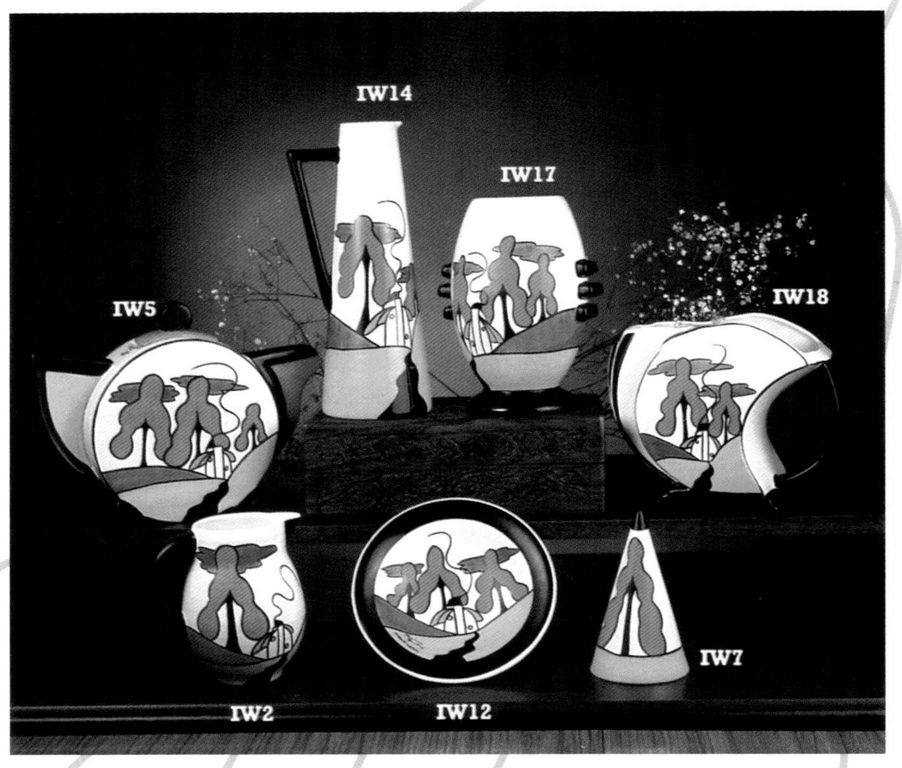

Round Tea-pot, Large Conical Jug, 3 Knob vase, Shell jug; Small jug, Mini comport, sugar shaker. See also the picture on page 37, which show a Cruet and a Conical cruet set.

Available in the standard set of shapes (see List of Shapes). Particularly rare: As it was only available for a short production period, many of the pieces are quite rare.

DIMSDALE HALL

April 99 – Dec 99 (Vase, Jug, Candlesticks (pair), limited periodproduction)
Aug 99 - Dec 99 (Toast Rack & Plaque)

"Named after a building in Wolstanton. It was a similar idea to Chetwynd, and as such was very popular." (Lorna)

DIMSDALE HALL VASE AND JUG

Open Stock

Dimsdale Hall Candlesticks

Dimsdale Hall Plaque and toast rack

Open Stock

Prototype charger (£320/$500, April 2000 auction)

Only generally available in the following shapes:
Vase (£50/$75), Jug (£55/$80), C/sticks (£40/$60 pair),
Toast rack (£28/$40), Plaque (£40/$60)

Particularly rare: Although these pieces are now worth 2-3 times their original price, it is the 12 eggcups and the sugar shakers, which were an Open Day Limited Edition special, that are particularly sought after.

OAKLANDS

June 99 - Oct 99

"Replaced the Marshland design. Oaklands depicts a stylised oak tree, and is named after a place near Porthill. Although only available for a short period, it was very popular, possibly because of the use of the colours red, orange, yellow and black." (Lorna)

DECO JUG, LIDDED POT, SUGAR SHAKER,
TALL THIN DECO JUG; ROUND TEAPOT, COMPORT, SHELL JUG

Open Stock

Prototype charger (£300/$450, April 2000 auction)

Available in the standard set of shapes (see List of Shapes). Particularly rare: Some of the older shapes, and the sugar shaker is always in demand.

Mirage

Sept 99 – Nov 99 (limited period)

"Mirage was the third of a set of three limited period designs released at the same time." (Lorna)

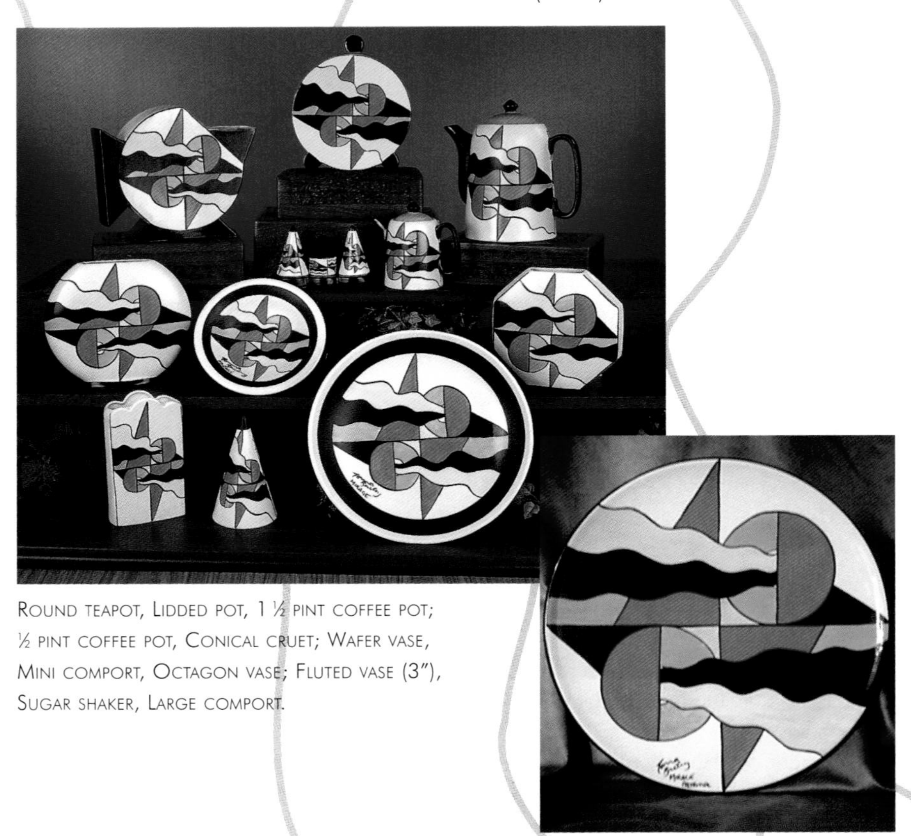

Round teapot, Lidded pot, 1 ½ pint coffee pot; ½ pint coffee pot, Conical cruet; Wafer vase, Mini comport, Octagon vase; Fluted vase (3"), Sugar shaker, Large comport.

Prototype charger (£200/$300, April 2000 auction)

Available in the standard set of shapes (see List of Shapes). Particularly rare: Specials like this charger.

Delta Giant Sugar Shaker

June 99

"Great favourite of many people (including Eric Knowles and Dave Lee!). It screams Art Deco! However, it took a lot of work to produce." (Lorna)

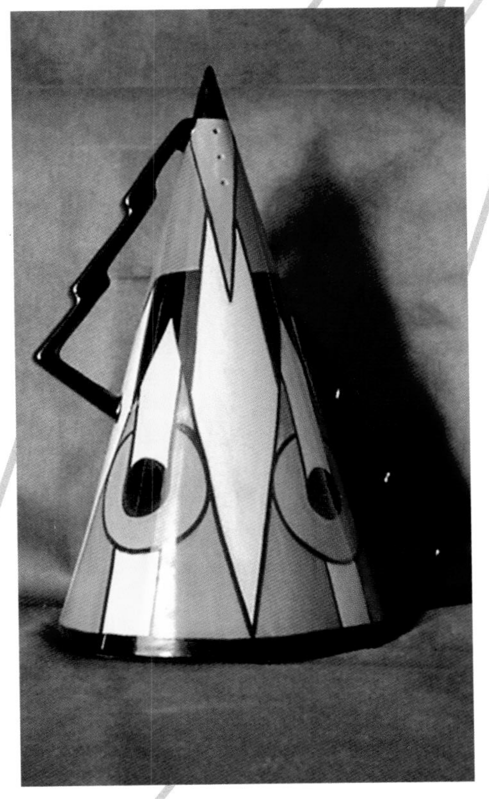

Delta giant sugar shaker

Available for One month only. 9"
Price - £75/$110. Fairly rare now, as it was available for such a short time. (now fetches £175/$300 at auction)

LAVA

Apr 99 - June 99

"The cruet was available first, but as that proved so popular other shapes were also produced." (Lorna)

LAVA CRUET

Available in the following shapes:

LARGE CONICAL VASE, GIANT SUGAR SHAKER, EGG CUPS, BACK TO BACK SALT & PEPPER, CONICAL CRUET, MINI COMPORT, TALL CRUET (PAIR), SUGAR SHAKER (2 DIFFERENT)

Particularly rare: The colourways taken to the Collect99 Fair.

Open Stock

Aspen

Dec 99 – Feb 00

"Aspen was released at the same time as Tropicana as a contrasting winter design, but Tropicana proved the more popular, as it turned out." (Lorna)

Upside down 2 semi-circle vase, Giant sugar shaker, back to back salt & pepper, oblong (3") vase and an octagon vase

Available in the standard set of shapes (see List of Shapes). Particularly rare: The more decorative vases and the sugar shakers.

Open Stock

Tropicana

Dec 99 – Feb 00

"Tropicana took the idea for Beach a bit further. It proved very popular." (Lorna)

Round Teapot, Rocket Vase, Wafer Vase; Rocket Sugar Shaker, tall cruet set

Available in the standard set of shapes (see List of Shapes). Particularly rare: Sugar shakers. Generally becoming more sought-after.

STORAGE

Oct 99 – 2001

"There were five different furniture designs which came in a choice of three colours, with a ceramic range to match. These were borne out of a demand from collectors for display options. I felt that the black shelves set off the colours of my designs very well." (Lorna).

(TOP) TRIFORM AND ROCKET, (BOTTOM) TETRAGON AND SMALL 'A'

Open Stock

Corner shelf units – they could be hung either way up!

(The last of the unpainted furniture was sold off in Spring 2001.)

Open Stock

StorAge - Ecstasy (back), Euphoria (front).

Shapes were called and priced as follows:

Euphoria Tea Pot (SA-1) £60/$90 (discontinued Jan 2001)
Euphoria Coffee Pot (SA-2) £65/$100 (discontinued Jan 2001)
Euphoria Jug (SA-3) £55/$80 (discontinued Jan 2001)
Euphoria Vase (SA-4) £50/$75 (discontinued Jan 2001)
Euphoria Double Vase (SA-5) £60/$90 (discontinued Jan 2001)
Ecstasy Tea Pot (SA2-1) £60/$90
Ecstasy Coffee Pot (SA2-2) £65/$100
Ecstasy Jug (SA2-3) £55/$80
Ecstasy Vase (SA2-4) £50/$75

"These were very much a new direction for me, very different, unique even. I still think they are some of my best designs." (Lorna)

Open Stock

Miscellaneous

1999

Egg Cups (EC1) £5/$7

Point of Sale (POS1) £5/$7,
and the Lorna Bailey video £10/$15
(still available from LJB!)

Limited Editions

Lorna's limited editions are much sort after. Most early designs were snapped up so quickly that many collectors never got a look-in. Even Lorna hasn't got copies of many of these.

May Bank

June 96 - Dec 97

"The May Bank vase originally didn't sell well at all, but was re-introduced at the January 1997 Showcase and did much better. So it wasn't strictly a Limited Edition! The early versions had a black band around the top. Of course, May Bank is an area beside Wolstanton." (Lorna)

May Bank vase and colourway (right).

Available for a limited period of time for £50/$75.
(Fetched £420/$630, colourway £450/$675, Feb 99 auction)

SUMMER GARDEN

Dec 96

"This was made for Ceramic Showcase 1997. It was a stylised foxglove. It was supposed to be a limited edition of 50, but only about 25 were ever made due to firing problems." (Lorna)

Limited Edition of 25 of 50! £50/$75
(Now worth £300+/$500+)

Limited Editions

Summer Garden prototype

Limited Editions

Aztec Large Jug
Aztec Small Jug
Inca Lamp base
Grecian Jug
Egyptian Jug
Roman Vase

Dec 96

Aztec Jug, Inca Lampshade, Grecian Jug, Egyptian Jug, and Roman Vase

Limited Editions

Limited Edition of 200 of each, although not all 200 were made:
Aztec Large Jug - £70/$100
Aztec Small Jug - £50/$75
Inca Lamp base - £80/$120
Grecian Jug - £70/$100
Egyptian Jug - £70/$100
Roman Vase - £40/$60

"Only 100-120 of the Grecian and Egyptian Jugs were made. Worse still, only five of the lamp bases were ever made. One recently went for £950/$1500 at auction!" (Lorna)

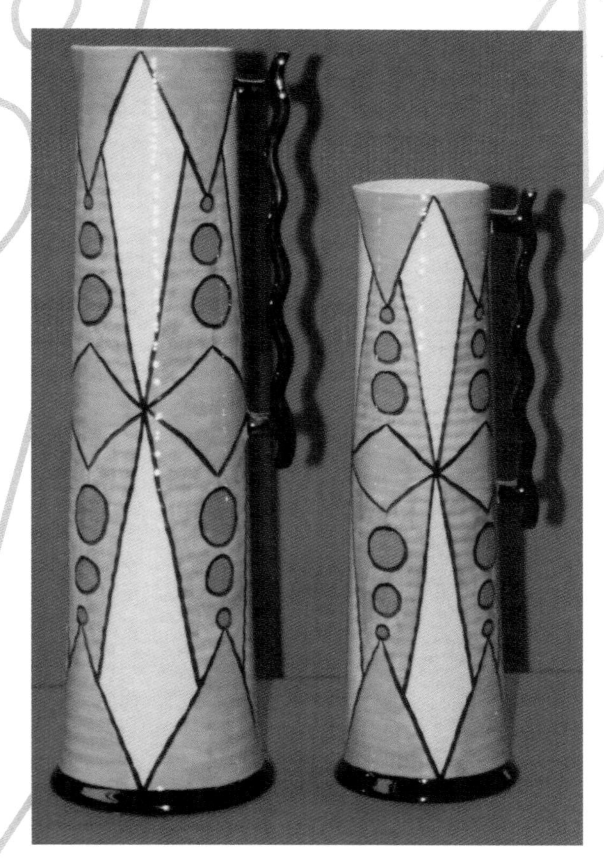

Aztec jugs

WATLANDS AVENUE CHARGER

Jan 97

"Watlands Avenue was a road in Wolstanton where Charlotte Rhead lived. (Lorna)

Limited Edition of 100, £50/$75
(Very sought-after, £250+/$400+)

Colourway sold at the charity auction at the Collect It! Fair, August 1998 (£1,100/$1,700)

PARK AVENUE CHARGER

Mar 98

"Park Avenue was a Wolstanton road in an opulent area of Wolstanton where pottery manufacturers such as George Wade lived. Nine chargers were produced with large purple trees by mistake. These must be fairly rare." (Lorna)

Limited Edition of 100, £75/$110
(£300/$450, November 99 auction)

LIMITED EDITIONS

Colourway sold at the charity auction at the Collect It!
Stoneleigh Fair, December 1998 (£1,000/$1,500)

CHETWYND CHARGER

Aug 98

"This, of course, was based on the open stock Chetwynd range. Although not strictly a limited edition, less than 100 were made." (Lorna)

Limited Edition of approximately 100 at £50/$75 each
(Now worth £150+/$250+)

Limited Editions

Charles Rennie Mackintosh Coffee set

Jan 98

"These were actual shapes from my college work. Only a very few plates were ever produced." (Lorna)

Limited Edition of 100, £200/$300

PANSY VASE

Jan 98

"Made for Ceramic Showcase 1998. This was an extension of the Summer Garden theme." (Lorna)

PANSY VASE AND INITIAL TRIAL PIECE (LEFT)

Size approx 6".
Limited Edition of 50, £50/$75

Inca God Face Mask

Jan 98

"Only 25 were ever made. In fact, only about two or three didn't have some sort of crack in them due to firing problems." (Lorna)

Limited Edition of 25/100, £100/$150
(Now worth £200+/$350+)

LIMITED EDITIONS

TWENTIES ELEGANCE

Sept 98

SET OF 4 PIECES: THE JAZZ BAND, OCEAN LINER, MANHATTAN SKYLINE, BELL HOP BOY.

Limited Edition of 250, £200/$300 for the set

Limited Editions

Mexicana Vase

Oct 98

Limited Edition of 250, £40/$60

Mexicana Wall Pocket

Oct 98

Limited Edition of 250, £25/40

Mexicana vase colourway, limited edition of 12 (left); Mexicana Wall Pocket and vase.

TEMPEST TEAPOT SET

March 99

"Tempest was very thunderbolt and lightning in theme. It was also the start of a Millennium inspired period." (Lorna)

Teapot, milk jug and sugar. Limited Edition of 350, £100/$150

ODYSSEY TEAPOT

March 99

"This is another personal favourite, probably my favourite teapot." (Lorna)

Limited Edition of 350, £100/$150

ART DECO LADY TEAPOT

March 99

"This was extremely popular as a two-for-one; a figure and a design in one piece." (Lorna)

Limited Edition of 350, £125/$200
(Now sells at auction for £200-£400/$300-$600)

ORBIT VASE

Aug 99

"This was another piece inspired by the approaching new Millennium." (Lorna)

6.5" high. Limited Edition of 100, £100/$150

CHEVRON JUG

Aug 99

"This was seen as very different, very ground-breaking, at a time that I was becoming so well-known for cottages! The name comes from the triangular design in the middle section." (Lorna)

12.5" high. Limited Edition of 250, £150/$225
(NB A smaller version was produced the following year)

FIESTA JUG

Aug 99

"This was from an original 1930s mould." (Lorna)

8.5" high. Limited Edition of 150, £75/$110

METEORITE CHARGER

Sept 99

"This was another Millennium idea, the idea being that Millennium meant The Future which led to Outer Space." (Lorna)

Limited Edition of 100, £125/$200

KALEIDOSCOPE CHARGER

Sept 99

"This was solely produced for those who had missed out on the Meteorite charger. It was only when it was finished that it got its name, as it looked like the inside of a Kaleidoscope." (Lorna)

Limited Edition of 100, £125/$200

MILLENNIUM VASE ("MILLENNIA")

Nov 99

"This design says '2000AD' if you look carefully!" (Lorna)

Limited Edition of 150, £100/$150

ART DECO LADY SUGAR SIFTER

Nov 99

"This was a follow on from the huge success of the Art Deco Teapot." (Lorna)

Limited Edition of 350, £125/$200

COSMOS SUGAR SIFTER

Dec 99

"Another Millennium inspired design, this time for a sugar sifter." (Lorna)

It had originally been made for Collect it! magazine.
5" high. Limited Edition of 350, £40/$60

GIANT TEAPOT

Dec 99

"One of these made £860/$1,300 at auction recently!" (Lorna)

Limited Edition of 25, £100/$150

THE LJB BAND !

1996

"There were terrible manufacturing problems, and as a result very few were made" (Lorna)

BLUE BAND AND WHITE BAND (BELOW).
(NOW WORTH £120+/$180+)

Commissions

Many companies have commissioned designs from Lorna. However, some commissions have been produced for individual club members or for the magazine Collect It!

Astro Rocket Sugar Sifter - "Collect it!" magazine

July 98

"Commissioned by Collect it! magazine for Issue 13. It was on the cover of the magazine, and sold out almost immediately!" (Lorna)

Limited Edition of 250, £39.95/$60

Bud Vase - "Collect it!" magazine

Aug 98

"Commissioned by Collect it! magazine for Issue 14." (Lorna)

Limited Edition of 100, £30/$45 a set

Limited Edition of 250, £39.95/$60

Crocker Buildings Salt and Pepper Cruet - "Collect it!" Fair (Newark)

8th Aug 98 (60 pieces) 9th Aug 98 (40 pieces)

Note: The Carnival colourway vase was also sold at Newark (see Carnival design in Open Stock section).
The white-topped cruets were sold to visitors at Newark who missed out on the orange-topped cruets

SOIREE JUG - "COLLECT IT!" FAIR (STONELEIGH)

5th Dec 98

"Kept blistering when fired. We went through quite a few before we got 100!" (Jennifer)

LIMITED EDITION OF 100, £60/$90

BACK TO BACK VASE & WALL POCKET FANFARE - "COLLECT IT!" FAIR (SHEPTON MALLET)

13th Mar 99

"The vase was the special Shepton Mallet fair piece. The wallpocket was the limited edition we sold at the event."(Lorna)

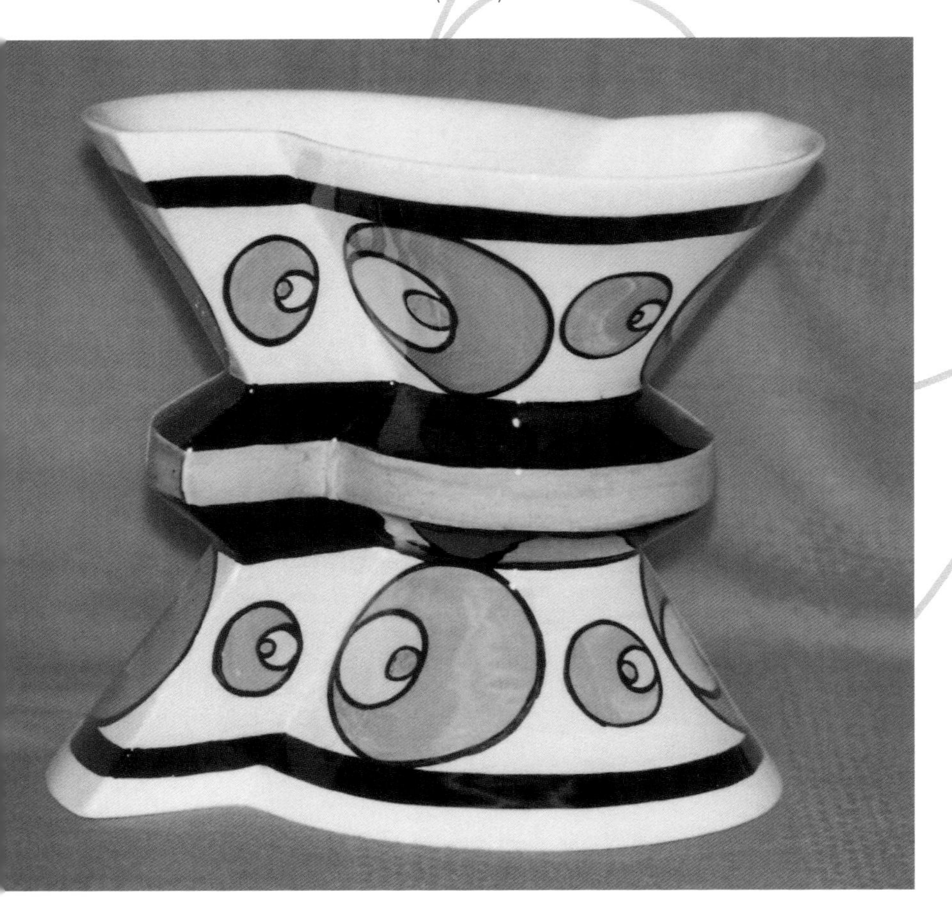

The Back to Back vase for "Collect it!" (£99/$150)

COMMISSIONS

Limited Edition of 60 wall pockets, £60/$90

ARABESQUE FLOWER VASE

Sept 98

"Arabesque is another favourite of mine. It's from a 1930s mould." (Lorna)

ARABESQUE VASE AND AN EARLY PROTOTYPE (LEFT)

Limited Edition of 250, £80/$120.
Commissioned by J&S Country Collectables.

COMMISSIONS

HOUSE OF HONEY POT

Sept 98

Limited Edition of 250, £75/$110.
Commissioned by Howard Pulford and Des Spurgeon,

HELTER SKELTER SUGAR SIFTER

Sept 98

HELTER SKELTER (RIGHT), COLOURWAY (LIMITED EDITION OF 12) AND PROTOTYPE (LEFT)

Limited Edition of 250, £40/$60.
Commissioned by Vic Jelenski.

CHARLESRENNIE MACKINTOSH ROSE COFFEE SET 14 PIECE

March 99

ADVERT FOR COFFEE SET

Limited Edition of 250, £295/$450.
Commissioned by Stockwell.
Stockwell reduced the price of the remaining sets in 2001 to £195/$300.

COTTAGE BISCUIT BARREL

March 99

TWO VIEWS OF THE COTTAGE BISCUIT BARREL

Limited Edition of 250, £90/$130.
Commissioned by Collectum (Geoff Tooze)

Commissions

Semi circle sugar sifter

Sept 98

Zulu Sugar sifter

March 99

Hoopla sugar sifter

March 99

"Hoopla was very much based on the fairground attraction." (Lorna)

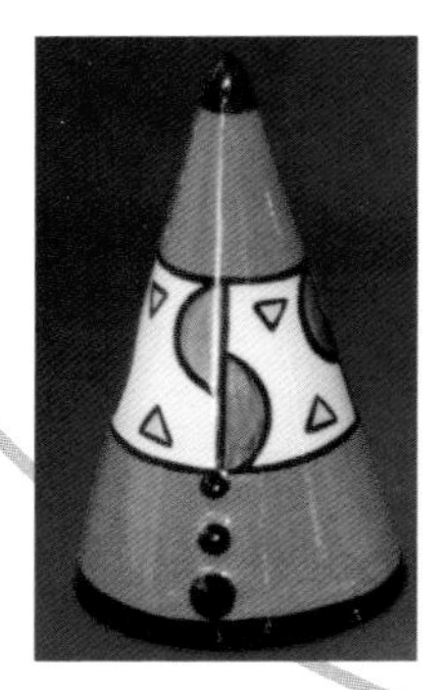

The Semi circle, Zulu and Hoopla sugar sifters

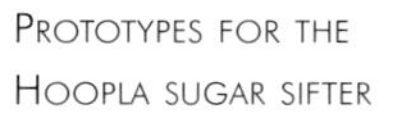

Prototypes for the Hoopla sugar sifter

Semi circle sugar sifter: Limited Edition of 250, £40/$60
Commissioned by F Eardley.
Zulu sugar sifter: Limited Edition of 250, £40/$60
Commissioned by F Eardley Ltd
Hoopla sugar sifter: Limited Edition of 250, £40/$60
Commissioned by Vic Jelenski

COMMISSIONS

WINTER (1 OF 4 SEASONS VASES)

April 99

SPRING (2 OF 4 SEASONS VASES)

June 99

SUMMER (3 OF 4 SEASONS VASES)

Dec 99

Winter, Spring, and Summer. All white trial of Winter vase (left)

Each was a Limited Edition of 250, £80/$120. Commissioned by Yesterdays

Eclipse Charger

Aug 99

Limited Edition of 100, £155/$230.
Commissioned by Lorne Spicer.
Sold out within an hour. (Now worth £220+/$330+)

CARLTON CARNIVAL CHARGER

Sept 99

This was a colourway of the Carlton Carnival charger. There were three different designs.

Limited Edition of 100,
Produced for Carlton for their open day. £125/$200

COMMISSIONS

COMET SUGAR SIFTER

Aug 99

Limited Edition of 250, £40/$60.
Commissioned by Peter Radcliffe. (of Foxy Lady)

COMMISSIONS

SHELL TEAPOT

Oct 99

Limited edition of 150, £69/$100. Commissioned by Conwy Teapot museum.

HALLOWEEN CHARGER

Oct 99

Limited Edition of 100, £155/$230. Commissioned by Lorne Spicer

BROOKES JUG

Dec 99

Limited Edition of 150, £45/$65.
Commissioned by Phil Brookes

APOLLO ROCKET SUGAR SIFTER

Oct 99

Limited Edition of 250, £50/$75.
Commissioned by Yesterdays of Watford.

Babylon Jug "Collect it!" magazine

Oct 99

Limited Edition of 150, £100/$150

Collector's Club Pieces

The Official Lorna Bailey Collector's Club, organised by Lorna and her family, was established in 1998. Listed below are pieces, many of which have only been available to club members, either by mail order or at special Collectors Club functions and Open Days at the LJB works.

Hill House Bud vase

1998

1000+ produced. Collectors Club members were allowed to buy two of these vases. £15/$25 (Now worth £100+/$150+)

THUNDERBOLT SUGAR SIFTER (BLUE)

Sept 98 - Feb 99

£35/$50, 1 of 4 (Elements series), 5.5", available for 6 months to club members.

SUNSET CONICAL SUGAR SHAKER

Mar 99 - Aug 99

£35/$50, 2 of 4 (Elements series) 5.5", available for 6 months to club members.

Collector's Club pieces

Twister sugar sifter

Sept 99 - Feb 2000

£35/$50, 3 of 4 (Elements series) 5.5",
available for 6 months to club members.

FIRE

Mar 2000 - Aug 2000

£35/$50, 4 of 4 (Elements series) 5.5", available for 6 months to club members.

Collector's Club Pieces

21st birthday party piece (Spiral jug)

20th Feb 99

£10/$15 Marked "TWENTYONE". Available at Lorna's 21st birthday party at The Kings Hall, Stoke-on-Trent. (Now worth £45/$70)

Celestrial Vase

Oct 99

Mini vase

Oct 99

Celestrial Vase (£50/$75),
Mini vase (£10/$15) - Oct 99 Open Day

INDEX